W9-ATC-233

This book belongs to

_____

Ready, racers? Pretend your finger is a racecar and that the alphabet inside the cover here is a race track! How long does it take your finger to make one course around all the capital letters. (While you trace each letter, a grown-up can be your official timer.) Inside the back cover, there's another race track: the alphabet's small letters. Zoom around those letters, too! For even more fun, make up a race just using the letters of one word. For instance, how long does it take your finger to race over the letters of your name? (The more you practice, the faster you'll go!)

ME, BC's

100 Ready-for-Reading Activities for Kids and Their Favorite Grown-ups

by
Michael J. Rosen
Illustrated by
Maris Turner

OHIO CHILDREN'S FOUNDATION

The Ohio Children's Foundation is a grant-making public charity that advocates for early care and education and has awarded more than $7 million to hundreds of organizations working to enhance the lives of children and their families.

Library of Congress Control Number: 2008939667
Third printing, 2014.

Illustrations: Maris Turner. Design: Gregory Hischak.
This is a revised, expanded edition. First printing, 2009.
Printed in the United States.

Ff

frog   fish, fly, fin, float, friend, face, four

You, Me,
and the
ABCs

Feel Free! You don't have to
know all the words to read this
book—or any book, really! Just hold
the book, turn the pages, and tell all
about what you see in the pictures.
Imagine what the characters are
doing or saying. Or make up your
very own story about what might
be happening on each page.

Hello! Here We Go!

Counting all the games, activities, and different ideas for sharing each page, **You, Me, and the ABCs** has more than 100 ways to grow alphabet smarter! Turn to any page you'd like. Skip around. There's no "order," which is why the one letter featured on each page isn't in alphabetical order. Wondering where to start first?

Are you ready to step outside for an alphabet game?
See pages 8, 14, 16, 18, 29, and 46.

Want to try a talking game that uses your ears and mouth?
See pages 7, 14, and 20.

Are you hungry enough to eat the whole alphabet?
See pages 10 through 13, 22, 24, and 54.

Are you on the lookout for letters?
See pages 15, 17, 46, 54, and 55.

hippo · **Hh** · happy

Want to get creative and
make your own alphabet?
See pages 9, 17, 21 through 33, 40, 42, 48, 54, and 56.

Are you in the mood to
really move? Games that use
your whole body are on pages 8, and 36 through 39.

Are you in a hurry? Then you'll
want ideas that are ready to go now!
See pages 1, 14, 18, 20, 26, 34, 46, 49, and 54.

How Was Your Day Today?
Before bed, take a few minutes and replay
your day. Tell about the places you
went, friends you met,
things you enjoyed, foods
you ate—anything!
Pretend you're reading
aloud from a newspaper
that's reporting about you.

Step-by-Step
Letters

You can walk the letters of the alphabet like an acrobat on a tight-rope. Along the way, your whole body will get to know the shape of each letter.

1 Draw a super-size letter with chalk on the sidewalk. Or scratch a letter in the sand with a stick. Or stretch some yarn or string into a letter on the floor. (Ask a grown-up to make the letters, if you'd like.)

2 Stand with your feet at the top of one letter and start stepping. Trace the whole letter with your steps.

3 Then skip to another letter. Try stepping the letters that spell a whole word! You can even say the sound of the letter as you shuffle along.

shark string, snail, starfish, shoes, sand, seagull, step, sandcastle, stick, shovel

Your Own ABC Album

You can save letters and pictures in a book with clear pages. It's just like keeping pictures in a photo album. Using old magazines and newspapers, you can make an alphabet book that changes each time you add something new. Sure, you can use an empty photo album. But you can also make a simple album with 26 plastic bags. (The quart-size kind that can be resealed are best.)

1 Have a grown-up staple all 26 bags together along the **bottom** of the bag (that's the side that doesn't open). Three staples should do it. (You could also sew or tape the bags together.) Each bag is for one letter of the alphabet.

2 Have a grown-up use a permanent marker to label each bag with a letter.

3 Cut out letters of different sizes and colors. Add words, too, and even magazine pictures or photos of things that start with that letter. (If you'd like, add a cover to your book: just tape your pages inside a folded piece of cardboard.)

Aa

an, ant, apple, arm, airplane, ape

Big Bowls of
Alpha-Bites

Use your noodles! Have some letter fun each time you eat alphabet-shaped cereal or noodles.

Try to spot the letters of your name in the bowl. Slide each one into your spoon and eat it—or see if you can fit all the letters on your spoon! (They might get scrambled before you slurp them down!)

What other words can your spoon scoop up?

Or try this: Dip your spoon in the bowl and see what letters you can get. Can you think of a word that begins with one of those letters?

Bb

bear   **bee, bowl, bed,**   **blanket, brown, butterfly**

What words start with a letter in the bear's spoon below?

 "**Toes** starts with a **T**. And **tiny**, and **Thomas**. And so does **tonsils**!"

Can you think of a word that contains two or three—or all of the spoon's letters? (You might want some grown-up help with that.)

 "**Bat** has two of the letters. So does **the** and **ant**."

 "And, look! **Hat** and **that** have all three letters!"

Take along a bag of alphabet cereal
for snacking—and for letter games, too. Most grocery stores stock alphabet-shaped dried noodles. They can be used in all kinds of word games or glued onto cards or painted.

Today's Menu

breakfast
alphabet cereal

lunch
alphabet soup

supper
alphabet macaroni
and cheese

Letter Toasts

How about toasted letters for breakfast?
Or a grilled cheese sandwich with your
initials for lunch? All you need is a
little magical letter paint ...milk!

1 Dip your finger, a Q-tip, or a new small paintbrush into a little milk and draw one or more letters on a bread slice. (Your writing will disappear...at least, for now!)

2 Have a grown-up pop the bread into the toaster or grill the bread for a sandwich. Presto! Your writing reappears on the toast as if by magic!

Tt tiger   toast, toaster, toes, teeth, table, tail

Letter Spreaders

Here's one more way to nibble your way
through the alphabet. Just add
cereal letters to any snack-time treat:

1 Choose any "crust" that you'd like:
toast, crackers, pretzels, pita bread…

2 Choose your favorite "topping":
peanut butter, jelly, cream cheese,
butter, honey, applesauce…and spread it
on your crust.

3 Press the cereal letters into the
topping. Spell out your name—or your
cat's name! Or put the letters in A-B-C order
—as many as you can fit—and nibble the
letters in order.

vine, vowel, Venus fly trap

Which Letters Whooshed By?

W w

walrus   whiskers, waffle, white, wrist watch, word

Pretend your ears can tune into different channels—one for each letter's sound. And pretend that you can switch to one channel just like that! Suddenly, your ears can pick out one letter-sound as people talk, sing, or read...on a bus, on the radio—anywhere!

Tell your ears to listen for one letter's sound. Pick **w** and you'll hear a whoosh of words that have a **w**-sound: **wish**, **where**, **water**, **whoops**, **wow**! Switch channels and tell your ears to listen for the **ch**-sound: now they'll tune into words like **church**, **such**, **much**, and **crunch**. Any time at all, just pick a letter-sound and listen in!

Eyes can have letter channels, too! Tell your eyes to be on the lookout for a certain letter.

Look at boxes, bags, and packages. Look in the mail, in drawers, on maps. Or tell your eyes to watch for common letter pairs such as **th** or **ee** or **st**. Or be on the lookout for a whole word! For instance, how many times can you find the word **word** on this page?

You can talk on a letter channel, too!

Try to speak in a sentence that uses one letter lots of times. Here's an example with **w**'s: "Would a walrus want a wonderful waffle? Wow! I would!"

To Do Today

Pretend your day is like a giant store. Make a silly shopping list of all the things you plan to get done today.

1 At breakfast, ask a grown-up to help you create a page with words or pictures of what you might do today.

2 Take your page along with you. Then, as you do each thing, find it on your list and cross it off. You did it! Add any surprising things you didn't know you were going to do.

3 At the end of the day, read off all the things you did. It's like a bedtime story of your big day.

Dd dog doll, dress, door, dragon

Shopping Word Spree

If you're actually going to a store, try this: Take a big envelope and fill it with pictures or words of the things you want to find.

Cut out coupons, ads, or pictures from catalogs, magazines, or newspapers. Then, see if you can match the words in your shopping envelope with the words on labels or signs at the store. (Of course, you can do this without buying anything at all!)

Word Hunt

An even easier game for store time is to choose a word and then hunt for it as you look down the aisles. Some words you are likely to find: **new**, **best**, **extra**, **size**, **real**, **now**, **extra**, **low**, **more**, **super**, **fresh**, **sweet**, **family**, and **large**. You could even count up how many times you find your word.

Eye Spy

You can play Eye Spy with any letter you pick, any place you happen to be.

Choose a letter. On a walk, look for it on mailboxes, street names, traffic signs, and store windows. In the car, try to find your letter on a map, in the glove box, or on the billboards that whiz by!

Or you can play Eye Spy with a friend. You spot something nearby that starts with a letter you choose. (Let's say you picked **y** and see a yogurt cup. Keep it a secret!) Then your friend tries to guess what you spied. Then switch! Let your friend pick the letter and spy something, and you guess what it is.

On these two pages, can your "eye spy" lots of words that start with **Y**? (Every page of this book has words that start with a certain letter you can spy.)

Yy yak yellow, yo-yo, yawn

Wait, there's more fun! You can play Eye Spy with colors! What things that are usually yellow can you find on these pages? (Things that aren't just colored yellow for this book.) Now, look up! Look around! How many yellow things can your "eye spy" right where you are?

Now, look up and around again! Is there anything right where you are that begins with a **Y**? (Here's one thing you'll find no matter where you are: **You!** **You** starts with a **Y**!)

You can play an Eye Spy game everywhere you go: the store, the park, a neighbor's house. You can even play it in bed before you go to sleep!

Daily Lucky Letter

Start your day with a letter—any letter—and then go on a hunt for it all day long. See if you can spot your letter in words you read. Listen for the sound of your letter in words you hear.

You can also do things that begin with your letter. For instance, if you pick the letter **L**, you can **look**, **leap**, **leave, lift**, or **laugh**.

For more fun, try a rhyming day! Pick one little word and then look and listen for other words that rhyme with it. If you remember them or write them in a list, read them at the end of the day like a silly poem. Let's say you picked **snow**: Your list might have the words **crow**, **toe**, **dough**, **low**, **row**, **mow**, and **slow**.

L l

lion   leaf, letter, ladybug, lamp, leap

Letter Faces

Once you've picked your letter, you'll find it everywhere, printed on papers, signs, shirts, stickers, even your dog's tags! And just as you can make different faces—and they're all still you!—letters can have different faces. The same letter can be tall or short, round or pointy, squiggly or blocky.

Cut out the ones you can and paste them on a page or tuck them in a re-sealable plastic bag.

Soft Pretzel ZOO

Make and bake an alphabet—and eat it, too! Any dough that you can roll out into a rope will work—cookie dough, bread dough, or even pretzel dough. Any favorite family recipe is fine.

Even easier: Use frozen bread dough from the store. You can find loaves, breadsticks, or even pizza dough to turn into letter pretzels. Make a few letters just to spell your name, or if you're really hungry, cook up the whole alphabet!

You'll need some grown-up help as well as:

some **frozen bread dough** (about 1 pound)

some coarse **salt** (it's also called kosher salt), if you want the pretzel to have a salty top

1 **egg**

zebra zipper, zoo

1 Thaw the bread. Once it can be stretched, break it into bits the size of big marshmallows.

2 Grease a large baking sheet or mist it with cooking-oil spray.

3 One at a time, roll a ball of dough into a rope about as thick as your thumb. Then bend or break the rope to shape your letter. A dab of water will help them stick.

4 Place each pretzel letter on your baking sheet. Leave space between the letters. Have a grown-up preheat the oven to 350°F.

5 In a small bowl, scramble the egg with a few drops of water. Dab a little on each letter with a paintbrush. If you like salty pretzels, sprinkle a little salt on top.

6 Now it's time for a grown-up to slide the baking sheet onto the oven's middle rack. Twenty minutes later, your letters should be ready: golden brown and crisp!

Once your pretzels are cool, they're ready to eat or to link up and spell a few words. (Just be sure to make each letter's sound before you bite off its head!)

A Nutty Clay

This simple nutty dough is super-easy to bend into letters. Just roll a small ball into a log, break off bits, and start "writing!" Then, to "erase," just roll your letters back into a ball or...gulp! down the hatch! They're edible.

You'll need:

1 cup smooth **peanut butter**

1 cup **honey** (or pancake syrup)

2 cups **powdered milk**

1 Put the peanut butter and the honey or syrup in a large re-sealable plastic bag. Squeeze and squish to mix.

2 Add about 1/2 cup of the powdered milk and mix. Do this three more times until the dough is smooth.

3 Now make a clean place to work: a large sheet of waxed paper, or a cookie sheet is great.

4 Wash your hands. Now take out a bit of dough (leave the rest in the bag to keep it fresh and clean) and knead it! Smash it! Make it smooth so you can roll it into logs and shape your letters.

You can also use any smooth cookie dough to form letters. But those need to be baked before you munch on them!

Nn **newt** nose, neck, necklace

A Stony Clay

This no-bake dough hardens so that you can keep your alphabet. Although you **can't eat** this dough, you can shape little letters to thread into a necklace. Big letters can be hung like ornaments. Or think of these as alphabet action figures and invent stories about your letters.

You'll need: 2 cups **salt**
2/3 cup **water**
1 cup **cornstarch** (plus a little extra)
another 1/2 cup **cold water**

1 You need a grown-up for these first two steps. Put the salt and 2/3 cup water in a saucepan. Just when the mixture start boiling, turn off the heat.

2 In a little jar or bowl, mix 1 cup cornstarch with the 1/2 cup cold water. Add that mixture to the hot salt water and stir quickly to make a thick paste. (If it isn't thick, stir briefly over a low heat.) Dump the warm dough onto a table dusted with a little cornstarch.

3 Your turn! Knead the dough—push it and stretch it until it's smooth. Then roll bits of dough into logs. Break them up to shape letters. If the dough feels sticky, dust it with cornstarch. If you plan to hang or string up your letters, use a toothpick to poke a hole in each one.

4 Let your letters dry. This could take two days. (A grown-up can put them on a cookie sheet in a 350°F oven. Shut the door and turn off the heat. The letters will be dry by morning.) You can paint your letters or glue and glitter them.

Knots and Knots
of Letters

A string, a piece of cooked spaghetti, a jump rope, a shoelace—you can change any of these into letters. Pretend they're letters that came untied—just like a shoelace. You can loop or twist them back into a letter's shape.

Make any letter you'd like by folding, twisting, or looping your "**string.**" "**Erase**" it by just straightening it out—then make another letter. Or see if you can change one letter into another with a simple twist or bend. For instance, the **K** becomes an **R** if you pinch the top ends closed. And the **R** switches to a **B** if you pinch the bottom ends closed.

Be on the lookout for other "**stringy**" things to write with, such as rubber bands, strips of aluminum foil, straws, tall grasses or vines, or ribbon.

K k
kangaroo   knot, key

Dots and Dots of Letters, Too!

Beads, dried beans, shells, pebbles, and buttons—a handful of almost any small object can make dot-to-dot letters. They're like your own marching band, spelling out letters or small words.

Just place one dot next to another, forming the lines and curves that make up each letter. See if you can change one letter into another by moving a few of your dots. For instance, if you took the dots on the left side of the **t** and put them on the right side, you could make an **f**, and spell the word **if**.

To "erase" your letters, push your dots into a pile and start writing again!

Can you see the three words that the insects have spelled on this page?

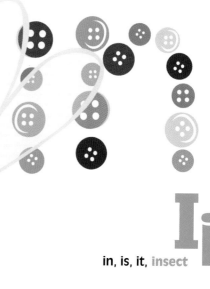

in, is, it, insect

Etch and Erase Everywhere

With just two things, you can create a magic page so you can write and erase as many times as you'd like, wherever you are.

You'll need:

your **page**—a shoebox lid, baking tin, a pie pan, or any shallow container with a rim

your **writing powder**—sugar, salt, flour, cocoa powder, bread crumbs, Jell-O, instant-drink mix...

1 Cover your page with a light coating of your writing powder.

2 Write your letters, words, or message in the powder.

3 Erase what you've written by gently shaking the page.

Ee

elephant egg, eight, eagle, eye, ear, eyeglasses

Outside, you can find all sorts of pages. Write with your finger in a sandbox or on a beach. Write with a stick in a garden, in pebbles, or in dusty ground. Write with an icicle or your mitten in snow. Write with a stone or a piece of chalk on a sidewalk —and then erase everything with a spray from a hose!

Squishy Letter Pillows

Here's one more silly slate for drawing letters. Place a little
shaving cream, pudding, tempera paint, cream of wheat,
or any other thick, squishy liquid inside a re-sealable plastic
bag. You just need enough to create a very thin pillow.
Seal the bag tightly. (Use tape to make an extra seal, if
you'd like.) Use your finger to write on the bag: a clear
letter appears as the goop slides away. To erase,
just smooth out the pillow again.

Printing Paints

With this special "paint," you can print letters and words on your skin—and they'll wash off easily. Write your name, a special word for the day, or even the entire alphabet.

For **Body Letter Paint**, you'll need:

1 tablespoon **baby lotion** (try Johnson's Baby Lotion or Pond's Cold Cream)

2 tablespoons **cornstarch**

1 tablespoon **water**

a few drops of **food coloring**, any color

1 small new **paintbrush** or a **Q-tip**

1. In a small paper cup, stir together the first 3 ingredients.

2. Add a couple drops of food coloring and stir. (More drops will make darker paint, which can be harder to wash off.)

3. Use the brush or Q-tip to draw the letters on your skin. A light coating is all you need. Then let the letters dry so they don't smear. To remove your letters, rub with another dab of lotion and wash off.

P p

pocket, pencil, pen, paintbrush penguin

This paint is perfect for writing on a sink, bathtub, or bathroom tiles. Finger-paint some words while you're washing up, and then...wash away your letters.

For **Bathtub Paint**, you'll need:

a little **tray** (a Styrofoam egg carton is great)

1/3 cup liquid **dish soap**

1 tablespoon **cornstarch**

a few drops of **food coloring**

1 Stir together the soap and the cornstarch in a small cup.

2 Pour the mixture into your tray. If you'd like 3 colors, put a glop into 3 separate parts of your tray.

3 Add 1 or 2 drops of whatever colors you'd like to each cup in your tray, and stir. Use a brush or your fingertip to start writing!

joy   jellyfish, Julia

You can also write on a "page" made of shaving cream.
Squirt out a dab, smear it on the counter or tile to make your
"**sheet of paper**," and let your finger be your "**pencil**!"

Your world is filled with other pages where you
can write and erase. If a grown-up says okay, write
with your finger on a steamy mirror, on a
frosty window, or on your car before it's
time for a wash!

Alphabet
Magic Trick

Your whole body knows how to read! It doesn't need your eyes to see the letters. Try this cool trick:

1. Close your eyes. Have a friend take your hand and draw a letter with a finger on your hand.

2. Can you guess what letter it is without looking? You can!

The rest of your body can read, too! Have your friend write a letter on your back. Or you just close your eyes and draw a letter on any part of your own body. Any letter that your eyes know, your whole body knows!

Ready for funnier fun?
Try drawing invisible letters on a table with your elbow! Try drawing letters on the ground with your big toe! You can!

Mm

mouse   **magician**, moon, mushroom, mother, mouth

Want to make this into a magic trick? You need a helper as well as someone to be your audience.

1 Stand right next to your helper with his or her arm behind your back.

2 Ask your audience member to point to a letter or word. But you close your eyes so you can't see it!

3 Pretend to think hard—really hard. (Meanwhile, your helper writes the chosen letter or word on your back, being careful that the audience can't see that!)

4 Then use your magic powers …and guess the answer!

Body-Os and All the Other Letters

Your hand can shape letters even without a pencil or a crayon! And guess what else? Your whole body can form the alphabet's letters by bending, crossing, or connecting your hands, arms, and legs.

Start with your two hands. What letters can you make by touching or linking your fingers? An **O** is pretty easy, and the octopus is showing you one way to make a **T**. What else can you form? Hold your thumb away from your hand and it makes an **L**—see it?

How would you make a **K** with your body? Unless you're an ostrich, probably not by looping your neck around another ostrich neck!

ostrich   owl, octopus, on, over, one, orange

What letters can you shape if you just use one arm? (Try a **P**, like the octopus.) What if you used both arms? (You can make another **O**, like the owl. And the **F** is easy, too!)

Can you make letters just with your legs? Of course, you can stand, sit, or lie down to shape your letter.

Extra
Body Letters

Now try to make a letter with your whole body. An **X** is easy: Just throw your arms out and up and slide your legs apart! Some other easy letters are **P, Y, F, R, K, C** and **Z**. Can your body form others?

What letters can you make with a partner? You and a friend can shape a letter together by holding hands, crossing or linking your legs or arms, and bending or stretching. The skeletons here are shaping an **A** together —can you do that? Try making an **M, H,** or **D**. Or try some of the small letters, too.

Do you think you can spell your name with your body? Just change from one letter's shape into the next one—it's your name's dance!

Xx
x-ray

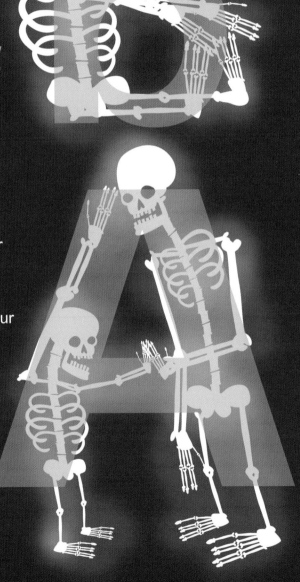

See what other words your body can spell, or try to move through the whole alphabet and make all 26 letters with your body! Try capital letters and the small letters, too.

Quick Alphabet Quilt

Cut out letters from magazines or newspapers to create patterns... like on pajamas or bedspreads. Or turn your letter-squares face down and play a letter-matching memory game.

Cut out a square with one letter in it. Use blunt scissors or ask for grown-up help. Keep your letter squares in an envelope and then set them out on the floor, a table, or your bed when you're ready to play.

To make a letter quilt, you create a pattern instead of spelling words. You're just arranging your letter-squares in rows. Try these patterns:

Capital letters next to small letters:

G e T x U q P
a Z w H m C I

Letters with curves next to letters that without curves:

O I Q L C H
T B V S X P

Upside down letters next to right side up letters:

A Λ C Ǝ E
Ⅎ Ɔ H Ʇ K Ⅎ M

queen   quilt, question mark, quarter

In the letter-matching game, you need a pair of each letter. The more pairs you include in your game, the bigger your challenge. (You can even choose one capital and one small letter for each pair—like **Q** and **q**.) Now, the object is to match each letter with its mate.

1

Turn all your letter pairs face down so you can't see the letters. Slide them around so you don't know where each letter is hiding.

2

Turn over one letter. Now guess where its match might be and turn over that square. Did you make a match? If so, take both letters off your game table. Good job! If you didn't, turn both letters face-down again and try to remember where they are.

3

Turn over a new square. Now guess— or remember—where that letter's match might be...and turn over that square. Were you right?

4

Keep turning over letters and guessing until you match all the letters and clear your whole game board.

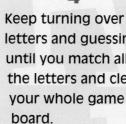

Umbrella

Sticker Your World

You can make your own stickers out of words, letters, and pictures you find in magazines or newspapers. It's three parts fun:

First you find the words. Second, you paint them with your special **glue**. And third, you sticker your world! Post your homemade stickers anywhere you like. Turn your room into a world of words!

You'll need:

1 packet of **unflavored gelatin**

1 teaspoon **vanilla**, mint, or other flavoring

6 tablespoons **water**

fish

1 Gather up your words. A grown-up can help you write them on small slips of paper, or you can snip words out of magazines or newspapers.

2 Swirl together the 3 ingredients in a small bowl.

unicorn **Uu** umbrella, under, up

3 Use your finger or a little brush to dab the back of each word with glue.

4 Let the papers dry. Then just lick 'em and stick 'em on any flat, dry surface!

When friends come to visit, give them a tour of your room and read off all the words you know!

Add or change words any time you'd like. And if any surface seems sticky when you remove your label, just wipe it clean with a damp cloth.

globe

bed

desk

bird

Cut-out Word "Clothes-line"

With a long piece of string, yarn, or rope, you can make a clothesline you can read. Just add on words and pictures using paperclips, clothespins, or tape. Every day you can hang out a new line to dry!

Have a grown-up attach both ends of your line—in your room, in the kitchen, in the yard. Anywhere! Then you clip on a display of whatever you'd like. Here are some ideas:

Cc

chicken   clothesline, cloud,   cat, cow, chick,   can, cheese

- Clip out giant letters from old magazines to spell your name.

- Do a string of words or pictures that all start with the same letter.

- Make a sentence with words or pictures that you find.

- Pin on words that all share one special sound. For instance, **crown**, **crow**, **cricket**, and **crib** all have the same **cr** sound.

- Try a rhyming clothesline! Clip on one word or a picture and then find others that rhyme with it. For instance: if you hang up a sock, you could add rhyming words such as **block**, **lock**, **rock**, **clock**, and maybe even **peacock**!

Reading the Rainbow

Pick a color, any color. Then, look around the room, across the yard, or out the window: Can you find things that are the color you chose? It's amazing! You simply tell your eyes to find one color, and they can!

Rr

rat, raccoon, rabbit, rhino, reindeer, red, rainbow

Every color comes in many different shades and blends and tints! Some are lighter, some are darker, some are mixed with other colors.

Look at the pages of this book. Many show off different shades of the same color. For instance, this page has many different grays: light grays, blue-gray, pinkish gray, dark gray. For fun, see how many different shades of one color you can find on one page... in this book, or in any other book you like to read.

Bingo Games

You can turn a game of bingo into alpha-bingo! It's easy! You can make your own small or even giant bingo cards any time you'd like.

1 Make a few bingo cards with letters instead of numbers. Any size or kind of paper or cardboard is fine. (A blank side of a greeting card is great.) Draw three, four, or five boxes going across. Then draw the same number of boxes going down.

2 Fill each box with a different letter. Any letter can go in any box, but make sure each bingo card is different.

3 Every player needs a nice pile of markers such as beans, stones, pennies, M&Ms, cereal bits, or grasshoppers. (Okay, maybe not grasshoppers!)

Each player gets one bingo card and tries to be the first one to cover all the letters in any one row. That row can go up and down, from side to side, or from one corner to another.

To call out the letters, use any book or magazine. Just close your eyes, point to a page with letters, and say the letter you're touching. Whoever has that letter on a card gets to cover it.

G g grasshopper green, ghost, game

Tic Tac Toe

Instead of **X**s and **O**s, you and a friend each pick a different letter for each game. Or try a game where you make the capital letter and your friend makes the small letter (like the ghosts in the picture here). The same tic-tac-toe rules apply: The first player who fills three squares with a letter —either across, up and down, or from corner to corner— is the winner.

A Note for Your Favorite Grown-up

You are your child's first teacher!
You're the one who knows best how to encourage
your young reader. The simple ideas below are meant
to give you some extra confidence and know-how.
Adjust them as you see fit so that they will work
in your home with your eager learner.

Listen Closely

- Find a few times each day when you can just listen and **talk together**.

- Put aside anything else that you're doing for the moment. No phones. No TV. No other people talking. Children need to **hear themselves speaking**. They need to see you listening so they can learn to listen.

- Show your child you're really listening. **Make eye contact**. Watch closely. Share your interest by smiling, nodding, raising your eyebrows. Kids need to feel comfortable trying words and creating sentences.

- You can **correct their words or sentences**—but only once in a while.

Talk Closely

- It's helpful to **repeat back to your child** what he or she has just said.

- **Phrase it more clearly**, if you'd like. This helps children know that they've been understood. It assures them that words can work!

- **Ask questions**. Ask, "Then what happened?" Say, "Tell me more," or "What else did you see or hear…?"

- Encourage your child to **give details**.

- **Use all kinds of words** when you talk. You don't need to use small, kid-friendly words all the time.

- **Speak clearly**. Take extra time to say new words several times. You can explain what a new "big" word means and let it be a special treat or a "secret" you share. Adopt new words every day— and **make it fun**.

Read Closely

- Figure out when your child is most willing to sit still and share some quiet time. Before bed? After lunch? In the car? Make that a regular time together every day.

- Read together in any way you'd like. **Let your child hold the book and turn pages.** Point to pictures. Point out letters or vowels. Ask things like: "What do you think will happen next?" "What would you do?" "What's your favorite part of this story?"

- After reading a book, let your child retell the story. **Ask questions about the story.** Talk about the story later in the day: "Remember? The giant in the story we read also had orange pants..."

- **Read the same story another day.** As the story becomes more familiar, encourage your child to read aloud any phrases he or she anticipates. Point to the words, too, as they become familiar.

- **Borrow books from the library**: easy picture books, rhyming books, ABC books—and longer stories both for reading aloud and simply for sharing. Keep them nearby.

- Show your child that you love reading, too, by reading alongside your young reader. Share something of what you're reading.

And take this book wherever you two go. Not only is it full of ideas, but it's also filled with words and pictures to help your young person master the building blocks of reading and learning.

Ten More
Tiny Things
To Try

Typing Time

Typewriters, computers, or even telephones all have the alphabet on their keys. Can you find your name? Can you pick out all the ABCs in order?

Eggy Paint

With a little paintbrush, you can paint letters on cookies, crackers, toast, or even chips. Just mix one egg yolk with a few drops of water. Paint your letters and then quickly toast your treat to cook the egg paint.

Lots of Spots

These pages are also full of patterns: You've seen tiny spots and polka-dots! You've seen thick and thin stripes! You've seen checkered patterns. Flip through the book again and see how many examples of each pattern you can find. And, look at what you're wearing today: Do you have any patterns on your clothes?

Dressed in Words

See how many letters or words you can find on what you're wearing right now. Is there lettering on your shirt? Are there words on the soles of your shoes? Is there lettering on a label inside your jacket or on your sweater?

Letters in a Flash

Take a flashlight to bed and draw letters on the dark ceiling. Or slide under the covers and read by flashlight in your tent.

Double Letters

Can you find words on this page that have two of the same letter right next to each other? (Here's one example for you: the word **letter** has two **t**s.)

Pick Any Letter

Look here, or on any page, and find words that start with your letter. Find words that end with it. Find your letter tucked inside words.

Topsy-Turvy Letters

Turn this book (or any book) upside down. Most of the letters look wrong, don't they? But you can find letters that won't look upside down. Yes, some letters look the same upside-down and right-side up! And, even more amazing, some letters will turn into other letters when they're upside down. Can you find them?

Get in Shape!

Look back through this book at any page and see what shapes you can find. Are there circles? Squares? Triangles? Tall rectangles? Wide rectangles? Or look around, right where you are? Can you see other things that have those shapes?

Pocket Full of Words

Just for fun, pick one word—any word!—write it on a slip of paper, and carry it with you all day. Keep it in your pocket. Put it beside your plate at lunch. Tuck it under your pillow while you're reading Show it to each person you meet. Just to be silly, you could write the word "foot" and keep it in your shoe all day. Or write the word "smile," and see if each person you see smiles when you show them your word.

MicHAEL

Scrambled Names

Write your name on a strip of paper. Snip apart the letters so that each letter is by itself. Now, close your eyes and scramble the letters. Okay, open your eyes and put the letters back in the right order.

Or try this: When you close your eyes, have someone remove one letter from your word, and push together the remaining letters. Can you tell what letter is missing? Replace it, and then try again with a different letter removed. (Too easy? Try scrambling the letters and removing one letter.)

Try this with all sorts of other words you can write out or clip from a magazine or newspaper.

Michael J. Rosen is the acclaimed author of some 35 books for children of all ages (and even more for grown-ups!), including **A Drive in the Country**, **Our Farm**, **Avalanche**, and **Elijah's Angel**. For over 35 years, ever since working as a counselor, water-safety instructor, and art teacher at local community centers, Michael has been engaged with young children, their parents and teachers. As a visiting author, in-service speaker, and workshop leader, he frequently travels to schools and conferences, sharing his stories, poems, creativity, and humor.

As a talented editor and illustrator, Michael has enlisted hundreds of other authors and artists to create 15 philanthropic books that aid in the fight to end childhood hunger, through **Share Our Strength**'s national efforts, or that offer care to less fortunate companion animals through **The Company of Animals Fund**, a granting program he began in 1990.

His Web site, **www.fidosopher.com**, includes information about his books and current projects, as well as images and poems about the cats, dogs, and wild things who share his 100-acre farm in central Ohio.

Maris Turner was born in Michigan and graduated from the Columbus College of Art and Design in Columbus, Ohio, with a degree in illustration. He continues to create artwork for a variety of clients. This is his first book for young readers.